How To Draw
101 Dinosaurs

Licensed exclusively to Top That Publishing Ltd
Tide Mill Way, Woodbridge, Suffolk, IP12 1AP, UK
www.topthatpublishing.com
Copyright © 2014 Tide Mill Media

Dimetrodon

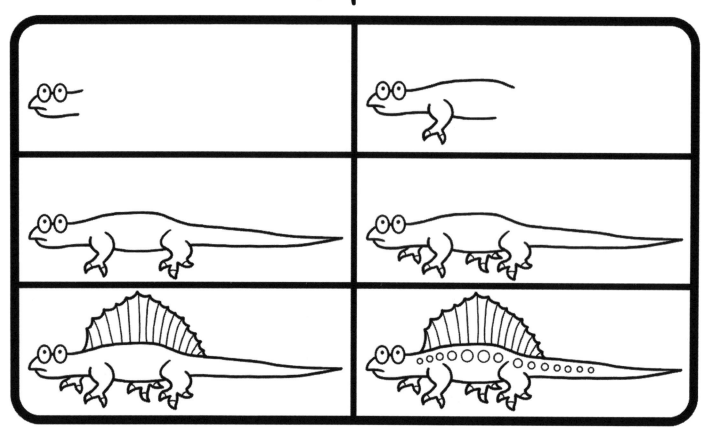

Apatosaurus

Procompsognathus

Pterodactyl

Ankylosaurus

Goyocephale

Isanosaurus

Ceratosaurus

Velociraptor

Iguanodon

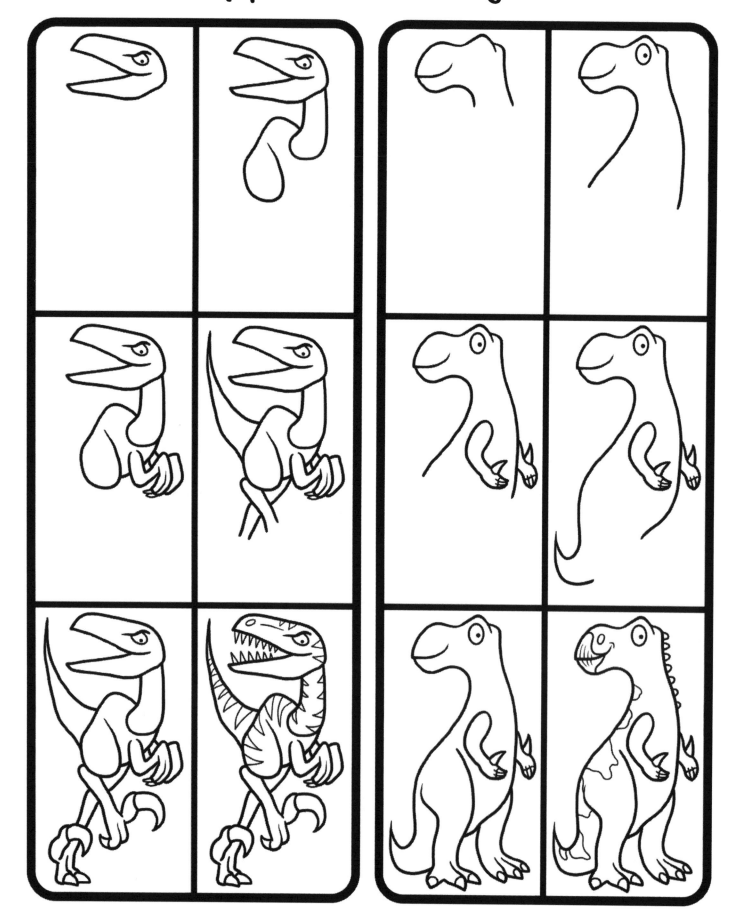

Diplodocus

Vulcanodon

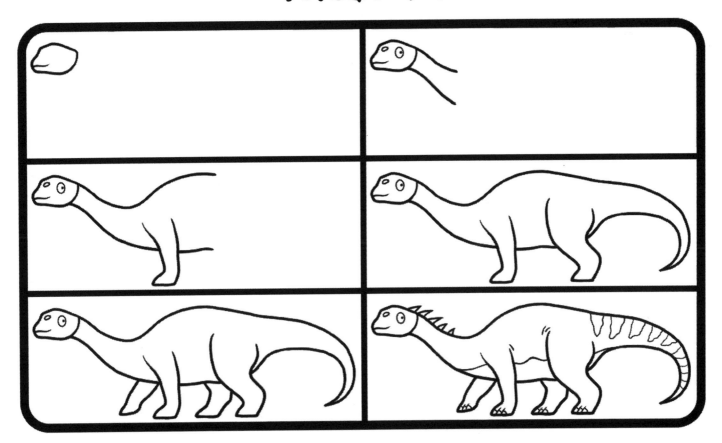

Brachiosaurus

Stegosaurus

Amargasaurus

Antarctosaurus

omeisaurus

Triceratops

coelophysis

ornitholestes

Muttaburrasaurus   Tyrannosaurus Rex

Pachycephalosaurus   Parasaurolophus

Troodon   corythosaurus

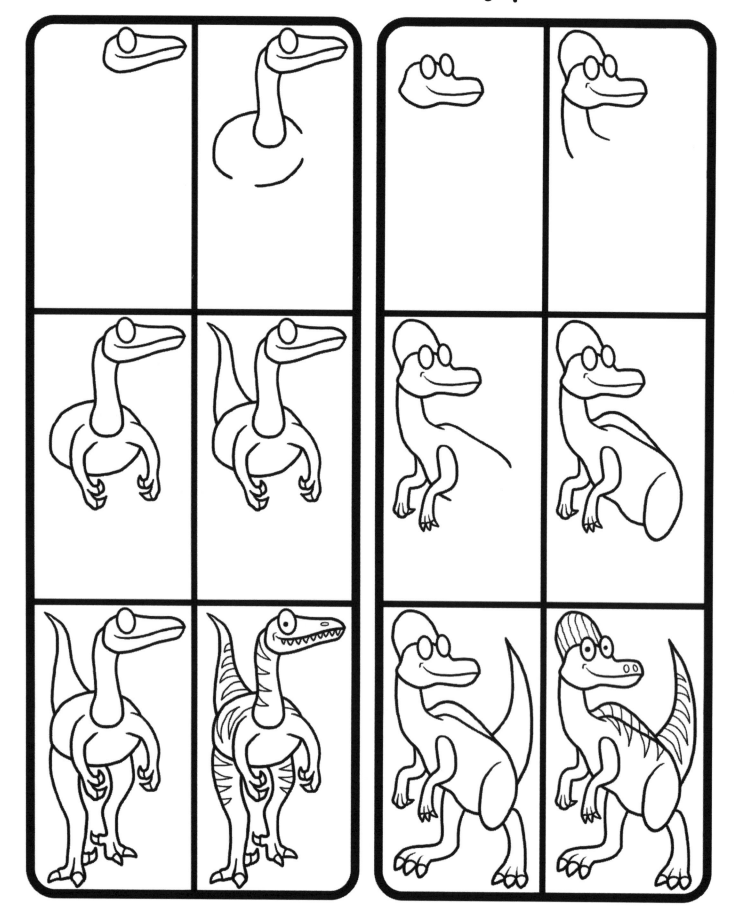

Elaphrosaurus

Hoplitosaurus

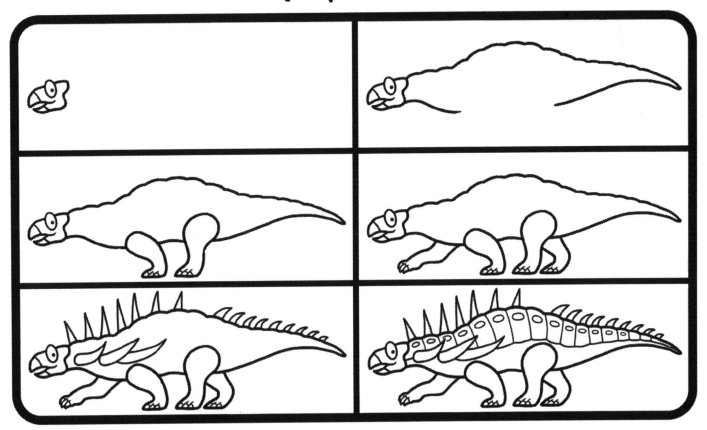

Kotasaurus

Labocania

Baryonyx

Carnotaurus

Chasmosaurus

Microraptor

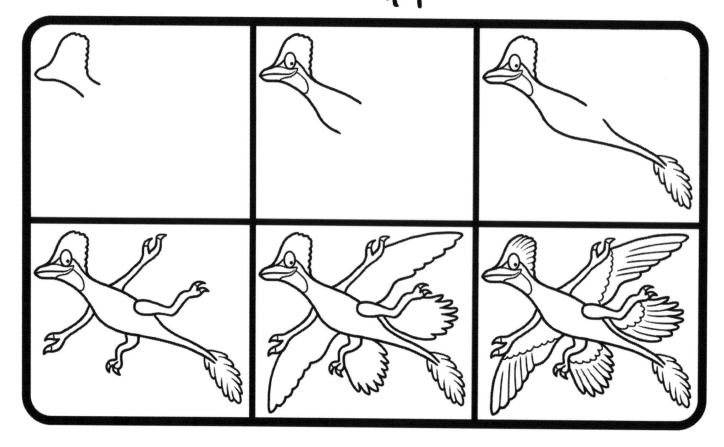

Erectopus   Garudimimus

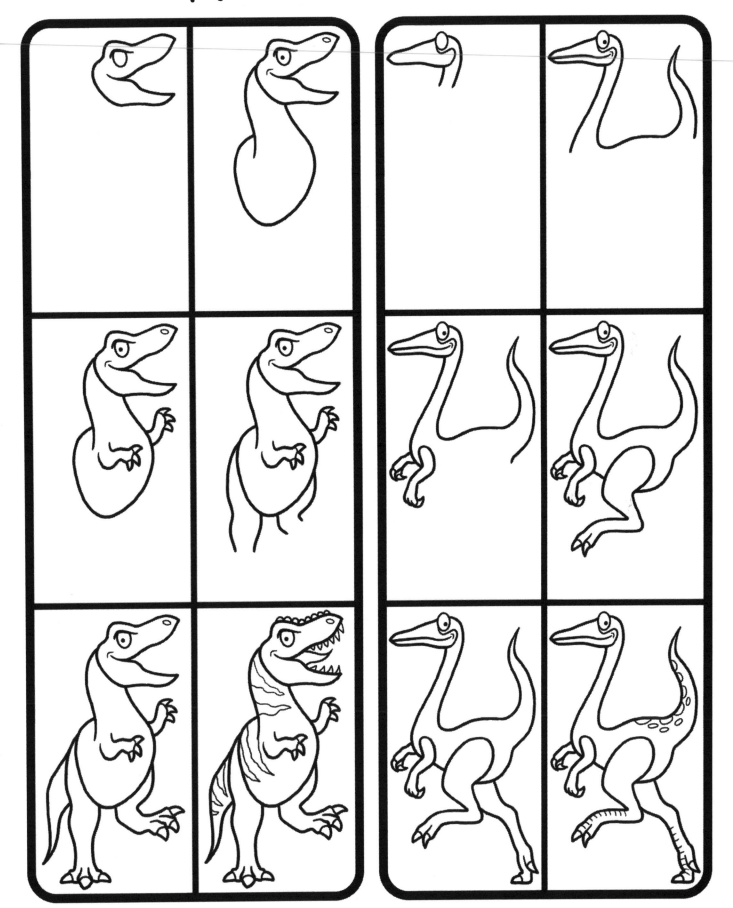

Indosaurus   Ingenia

Malawisaurus

Mongolosaurus

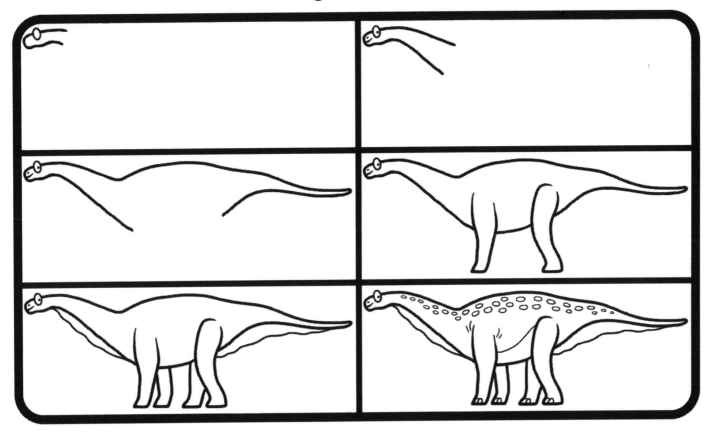

Nemegtosaurus

Nipponosaurus

Deinonychus

Gallimimus

ouranosaurus

Liopleurodon

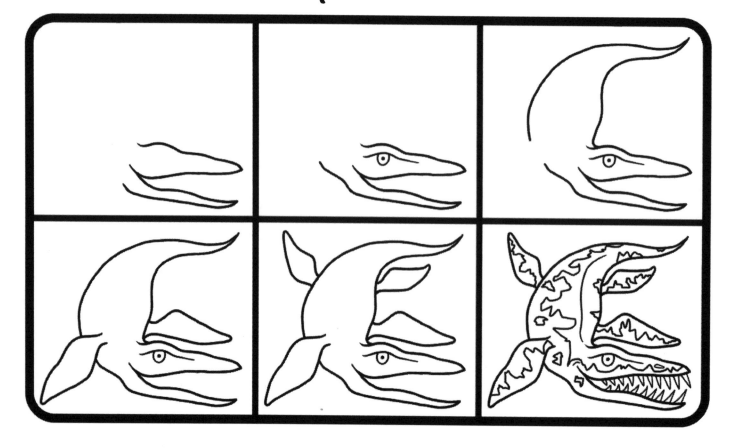

Jaxartosaurus   Lambeosaurus

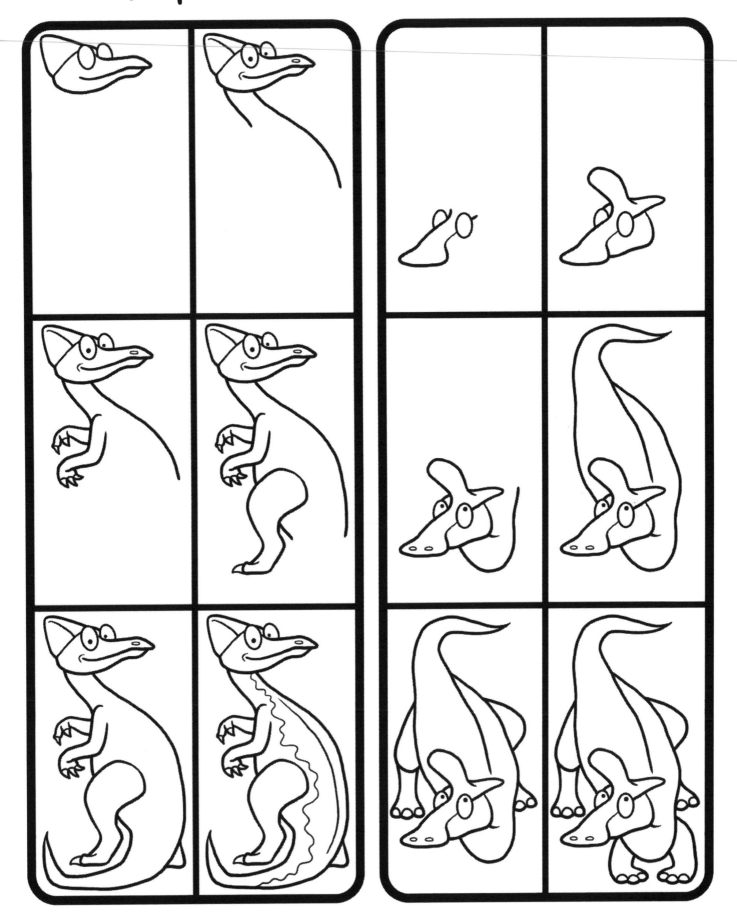

Laplatasaurus   Lukousaurus

Neuquensaurus

Orodromeus

Patagosaurus

Supersaurus

Protoceratops

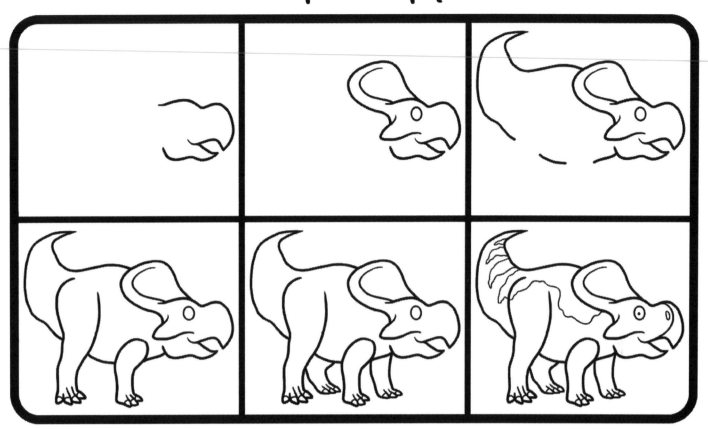

Psittacosaurus

Spinosaurus

Archaeopteryx

Tarbosaurus   Mononykus

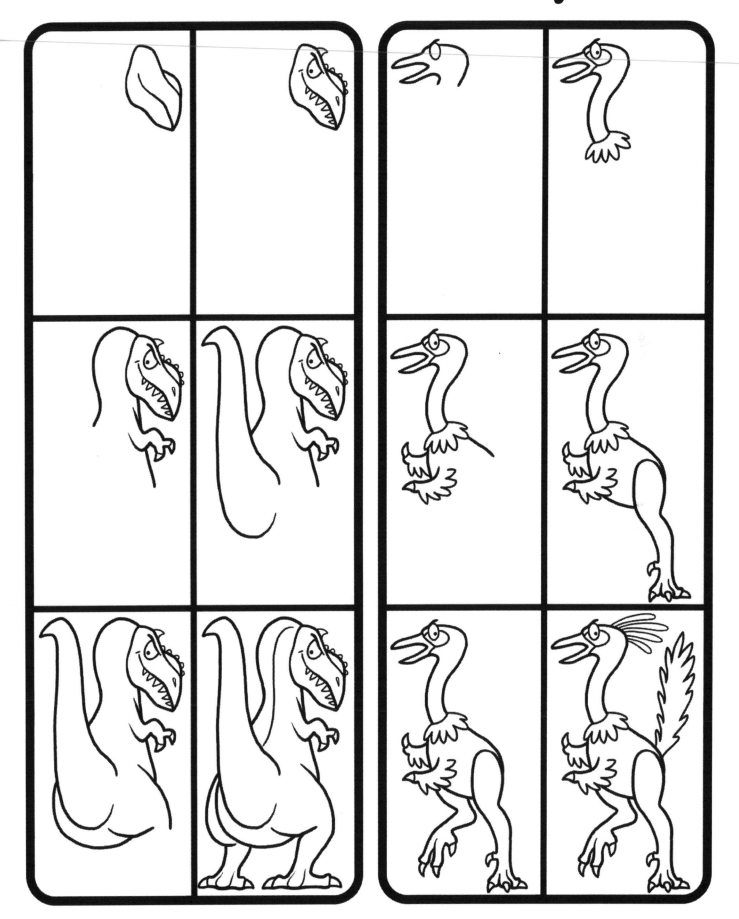

Lophostropheus

Sarcolestes

Titanosaurus

Quetzalcoatlus

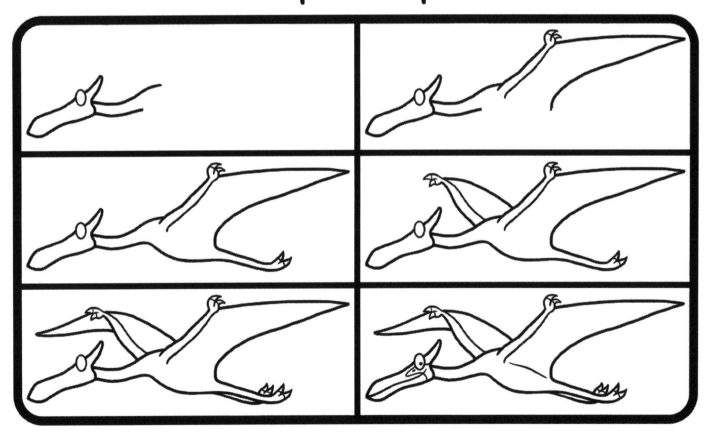

Peteinosaurus

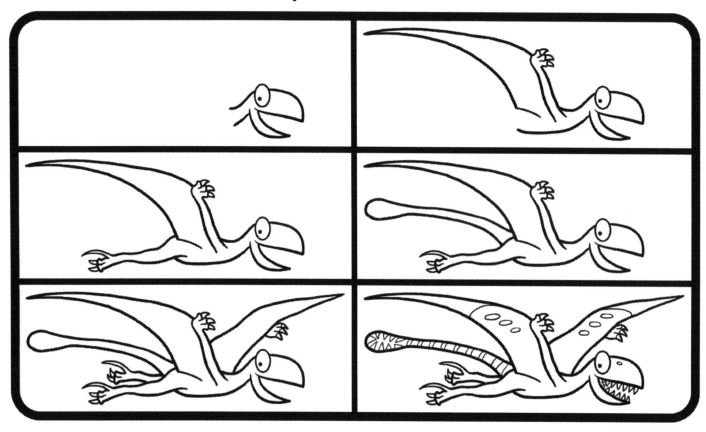

Mussaurus

Kentrosaurus

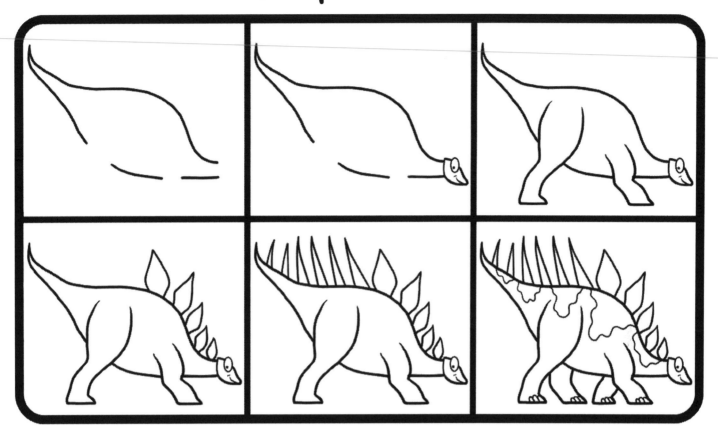

Bagaceratops

conchoraptor

Allosaurus

Stokesosaurus

Syntarsus

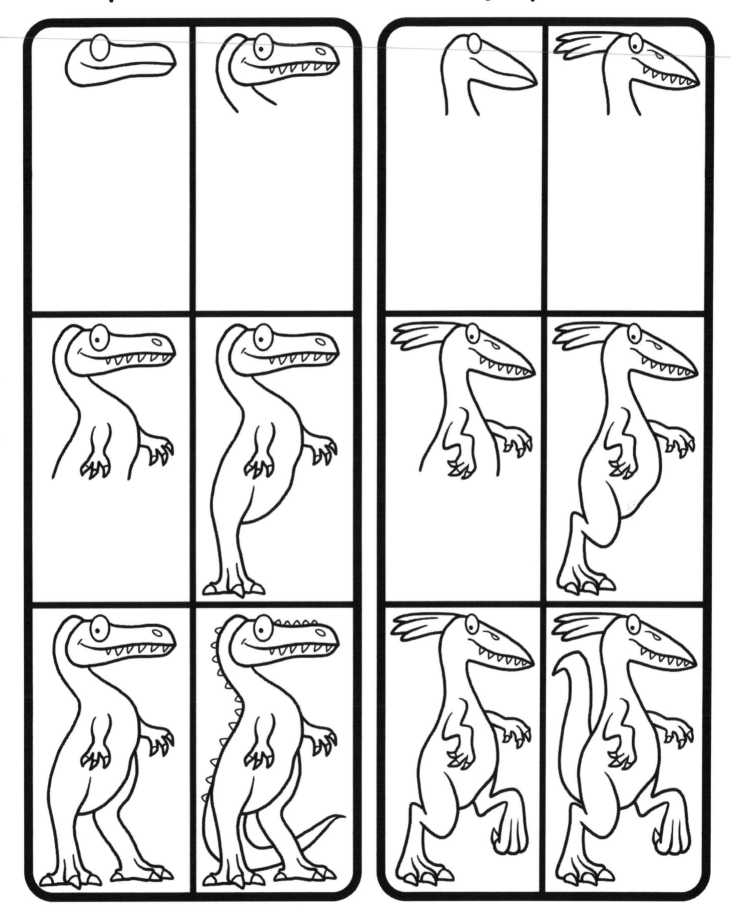

Wannanosaurus   Xiaosaurus

Rebbachisaurus

Megalosaurus

Maiasaura

Oviraptor

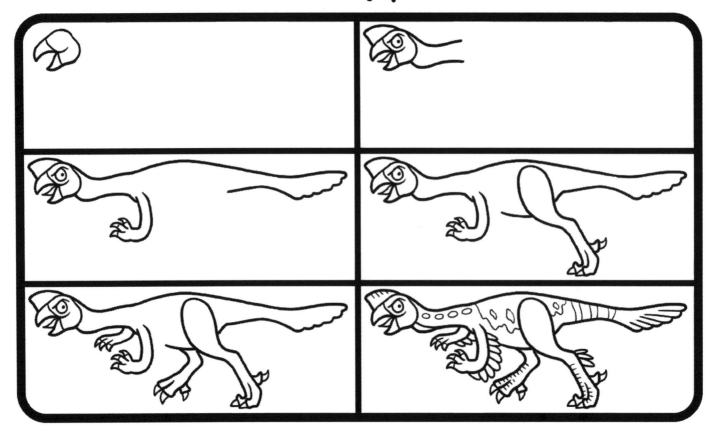

Datousaurus

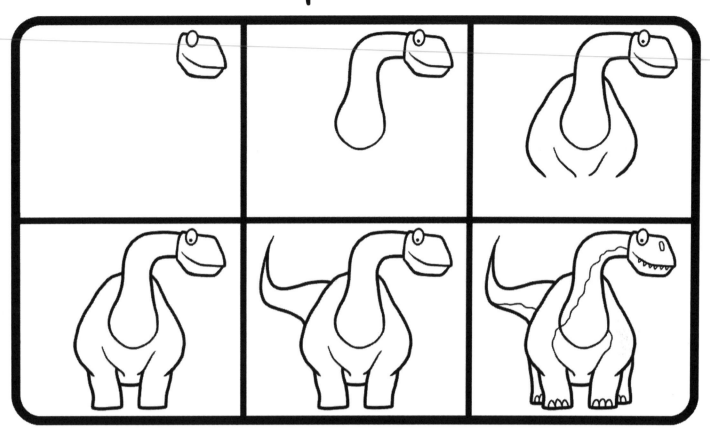

Gryposaurus

Avisaurus

Basilosaurus

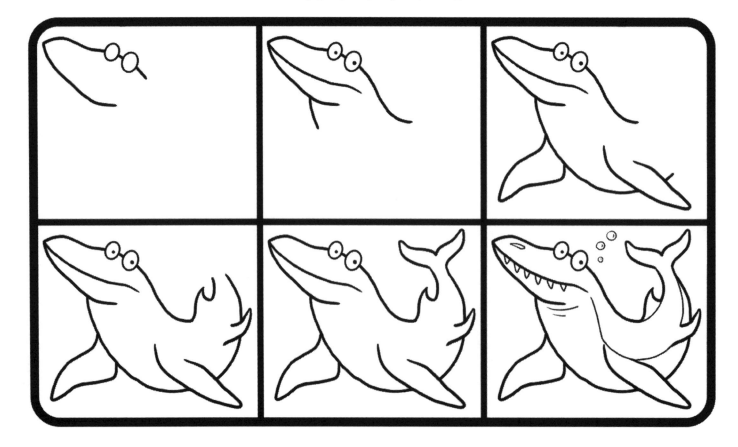

Zephyrosaurus   Rahonavis

Rhamphorhynchus　　Dilophosaurus

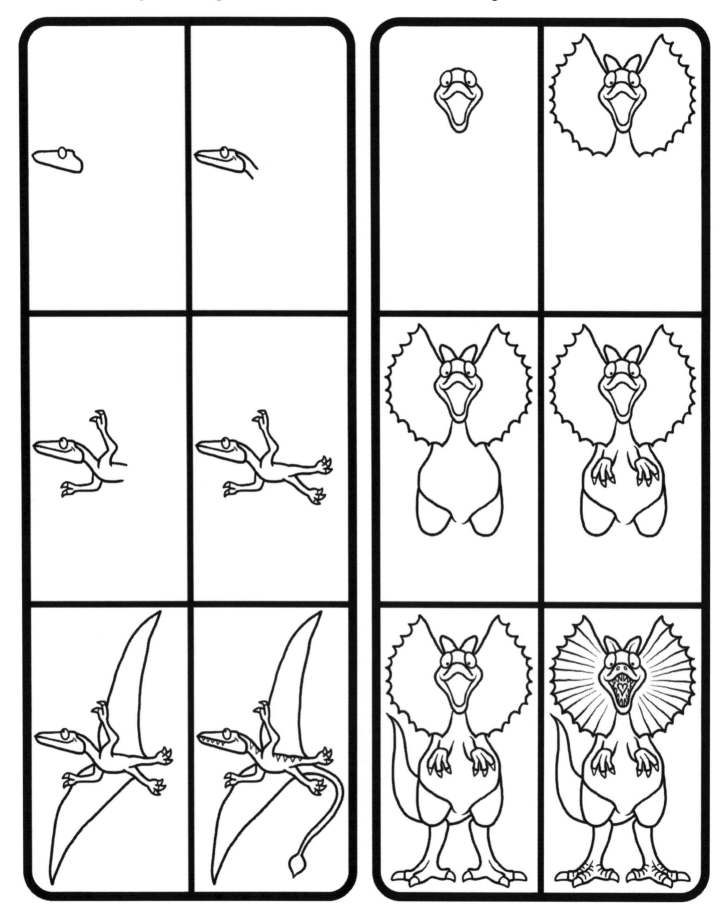

Stenopelix

Baby Dinosaur

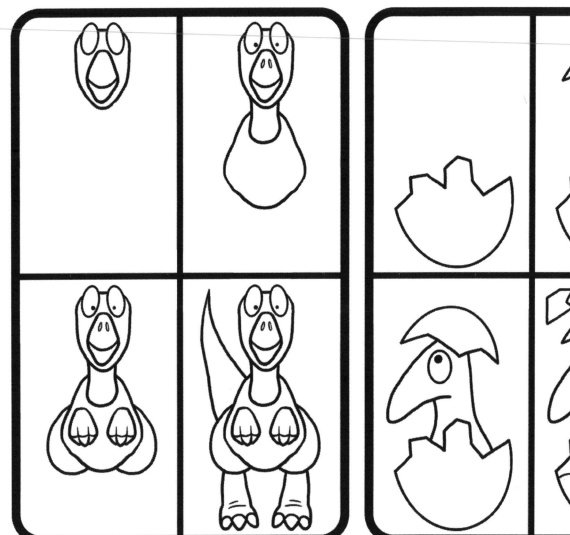

Estemmenosuchus

Ammosaurus

Yinlong

Antarctopelta

Archaeoceratops

Isisaurus

Sinocalliopteryx

Staurikosaurus

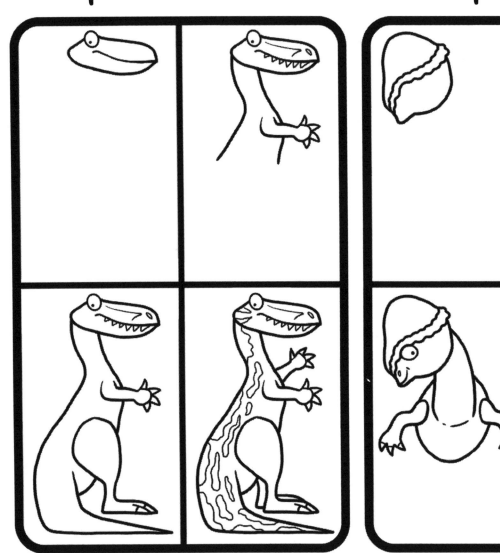

Stegoceras

Dracorex

Hypsilophodon

Harpymimus

Mauisaurus

Other titles in the 'How to draw' series:

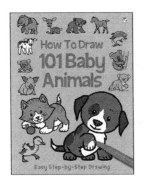
978-1-84956-987-3

978-1-84956-608-7

978-1-78244-484-8

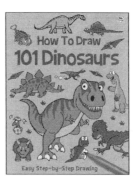
978-1-78244-021-5

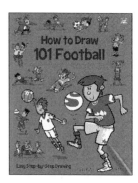
978-1-78244-536-4

978-1-84956-605-6

978-1-84956-607-0

978-1-84956-988-0

978-1-78244-486-2

978-1-78244-485-5

978-1-84956-616-2

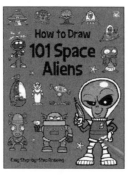
978-1-78244-483-1

978-1-84956-989-7

Practice Page

Practice Page

Printed in Great Britain
by Amazon